For More Coloring Book
and Giveaways
Please Visit
www.RelaxingColoring.com

THIS BOOK BELONGS TO

_____

Sign Up at RelaxingColoring.com
and Get Free Printable Coloring Pages!

Sign Up at RelaxingColoring.com
and Get Free Printable Coloring Pages!

Sign Up at RelaxingColoring.com
and Get Free Printable Coloring Pages!

Sign Up at RelaxingColoring.com
and Get Free Printable Coloring Pages!

Sign Up at RelaxingColoring.com
and Get Free Printable Coloring Pages!

Sign Up at RelaxingColoring.com
and Get Free Printable Coloring Pages!

Sign Up at RelaxingColoring.com
and Get Free Printable Coloring Pages!

Sign Up at RelaxingColoring.com
and Get Free Printable Coloring Pages!

Sign Up at RelaxingColoring.com
and Get Free Printable Coloring Pages!

Sign Up at RelaxingColoring.com
and Get Free Printable Coloring Pages!

Sign Up at RelaxingColoring.com
and Get Free Printable Coloring Pages!

Sign Up at RelaxingColoring.com
and Get Free Printable Coloring Pages!

Sign Up at RelaxingColoring.com
and Get Free Printable Coloring Pages!

Sign Up at RelaxingColoring.com
and Get Free Printable Coloring Pages!

Sign Up at RelaxingColoring.com
and Get Free Printable Coloring Pages!

Sign Up at RelaxingColoring.com
and Get Free Printable Coloring Pages!

Sign Up at RelaxingColoring.com
and Get Free Printable Coloring Pages!

Sign Up at RelaxingColoring.com
and Get Free Printable Coloring Pages!

Sign Up at RelaxingColoring.com
and Get Free Printable Coloring Pages!

Sign Up at RelaxingColoring.com
and Get Free Printable Coloring Pages!

Sign Up at RelaxingColoring.com
and Get Free Printable Coloring Pages!

Sign Up at RelaxingColoring.com
and Get Free Printable Coloring Pages!

Sign Up at RelaxingColoring.com
and Get Free Printable Coloring Pages!

Sign Up at RelaxingColoring.com
and Get Free Printable Coloring Pages!

Sign Up at RelaxingColoring.com
and Get Free Printable Coloring Pages!

JUST FOR YOU

Sign Up at RelaxingColoring.com
and Get Free Printable Coloring Pages!

Sign Up at RelaxingColoring.com
and Get Free Printable Coloring Pages!

CPSIA information can be obtained
at www.ICGtesting.com
Printed in the USA
BVHW062151301121
622779BV00006B/381